Ant
Friends

by Fay Robinson / illustrated by Richard Bernal

Harcourt

Orlando   Boston   Dallas   Chicago   San Diego

www.harcourtschool.com

Once there were 12 ant friends.
5 of them were red ants.
7 of them were black ants.

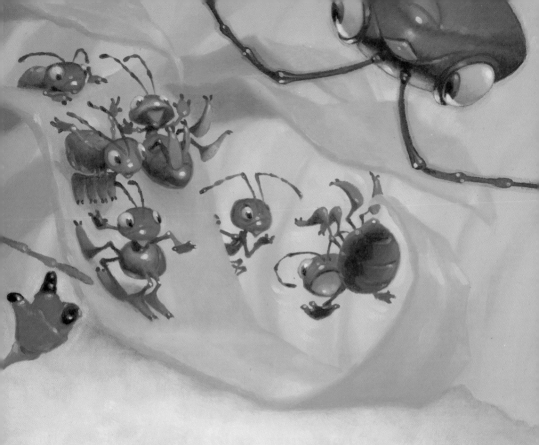

"We are red ants and black ants.
We are 12 ant friends!" they sang.

3

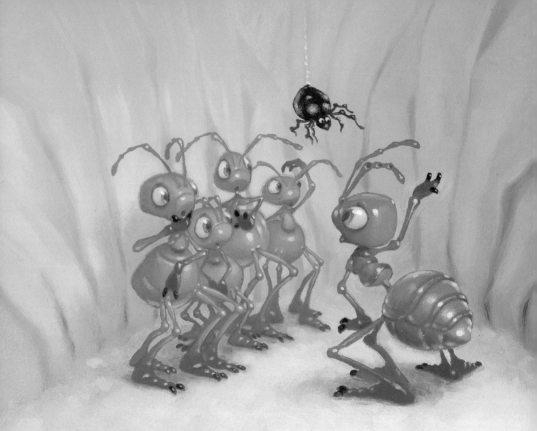

One day, a red ant said,
"We are not all here."
"How many black ants are missing?"

At the same time, a black ant said,
"We are not all here."
"How many red ants are missing?"

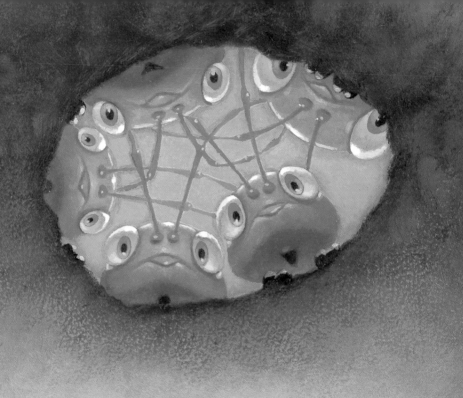

"We must find the black ants,"
said the red ants.

6

"We must find the red ants,"
said the black ants.

The red ants smelled apples.
The black ants smelled pie.
"PICNIC!" they yelled.

"Here you are!" said the red ants.

"Here you are!" said the black ants.
They sang, "We are 5 red ants
and 7 black ants.
We are 12 ant friends!"

Then they began to to eat!